THIS JOURNAL BELO

- -

- -

Happy Birthday
to my Best Queen in the world.

Date : .... ♡♡♡♡♡♡♡

IN GOOD TIMES AND BAD, I'LL ALWAYS BE BY YOUR SIDE. HAPPY BADY

Date : .... ♡♡♡♡♡♡♡

I AM SO GRATEFUL THAT YOU ARE A PART OF MY LIFE. ALL THE BEST ON YOUR BIRTHDAY!

Date : ....

♡♡♡♡♡♡♡

WISHING YOU MANY BLESSINGS ON YOUR BIRTHDAY. WE MISS YOU!

Date : .... ♡♡♡♡♡♡♡

Today is about you. I can't wait to celebrate you all day long!

Date : _____

♡♡♡♡♡♡♡

HAPPY BIRTHDAY! YOU DESERVE ALL THE CAKES, LOVE, HUGS AND HAPPINESS TODAY

Date : .... ♡♡♡♡♡♡♡

You look younger than ever! Happy birthday!

Date : .... ♡♡♡♡♡♡♡

On your birthday I wish you success and endless happiness!

Date : ....

♡♡♡♡♡♡♡

MAY YOUR BIRTHDAY AND YOUR LIFE BE AS WONDERFUL AS YOU ARE

Date : .... ♡♡♡♡♡♡♡

WHEN I'M WITH YOU I HAVE MORE FUN THAN WHEN I'M WITH ANYONE ELSE!

Date : .... ♡♡♡♡♡♡♡

You've always been there for me, and I will always be there for you

Date : ....

♡♡♡♡♡♡♡

NEVER THINK YOU ARE ALONE, I AM ALWAYS THERE FOR ALL YOUR FIXES.

Date : .... ♡♡♡♡♡♡♡

YOU HAVE BEEN THERE IN MY LIFE AS A GUIDING LIGHT. STAY BLESSED.

Date : ....

♡♡♡♡♡♡♡

KEEP SMILING, BE HAPPY, AND MAKE ALL YOUR DREAM COMES TRUE IN COMING YEARS

Date : _____   ♡♡♡♡♡♡♡

HAPPY BIRTHDAY TO THE MOST BEAUTIFUL PERSON I HAVE EVER MEET ON THIS EARTH

Date : .... ♡♡♡♡♡♡♡

TODAY IS YOUR DAY. MAY ALL YOUR BIRTHDAY WISHES COME TRUE!

Date : ....

♡♡♡♡♡♡♡

I WISH YOU LOTS OF HAPPINESS AND GOOD HEALTH IN THE YEARS TO COME!

Date : .... ♡♡♡♡♡♡♡

I WANTED TO WISH YOU GOOD LUCK IN YOUR FUTURE ENDEAVORS AND A FANTASTIC BIRTHDAY!

Date : .... ♡♡♡♡♡♡♡

MEETING YOU IS THE BEST THING THAT EVER HAPPENED IN MY LIFE. HAPPY BIRTHDAY!

Date : ....

TODAY I WISH YOU A FUN TIME, SHARED WITH YOUR DEAR ONES, AND A LIFELONG HAPPINESS!

Date : ....

♡♡♡♡♡♡♡

WISHING YOU A WONDERFUL DAY AND ALL THE MOST AMAZING THINGS ON YOUR BIG DAY!

Date : .... ♡♡♡♡♡♡♡

HOPE YOUR BIRTHDAY IS AS WONDERFUL AND EXTRAORDINARY AS YOU ARE

Date : .... ♡♡♡♡♡♡♡

WISHING A HAPPY BIRTHDAY TO THE BEST PERSON I'VE EVER MET IN THIS WORLD.

Date : ....

♡♡♡♡♡♡♡

WISHING YOU THE ABUNDANCE OF FUN AND GLORY, HAPPY BIRTHDAY!

Date : ....

♡♡♡♡♡♡♡

MAY THIS DAY BE SO HAPPY THAT SMILE NEVER FADES AWAY FROM YOUR FACE.

Date : .... ♡♡♡♡♡♡♡

HOPE YOUR BIRTHDAY IS JUST LIKE YOU...TOTALLY FREAKING AWESOME.

Date : ....   ♡♡♡♡♡♡♡

EVERYBODY HAS BIRTHDAYS. YOU JUST WEAR YOURS BETTER THAN MOST!

♡♡♡♡♡♡♡

YOU WERE BORN, AND THE WORLD BECAME A BETTER PLACE.

Date : .... ♡♡♡♡♡♡♡

YOU'RE NOT OLDER — YOU'RE JUST MORE DISTINGUISHED.

Date : ....

♡♡♡♡♡♡♡

MAY YOU ENJOY YOUR SPECIAL DAY TO THE FULLEST EXTENT, BUDDY!

Date : .... ♡♡♡♡♡♡♡

MAY YOUR BIRTHDAY MARK THE BEGINNING OF A WONDERFUL PERIOD OF TIME IN YOUR LIFE

Date : ....

♡♡♡♡♡♡♡

YOU ARE LOOKING SHARP! YOU WEAR YOUR BIRTHDAY BETTER THAN MOST!

Date : ....   ♡♡♡♡♡♡♡

THE WORLD IS A BETTER PLACE SINCE YOU'VE BEEN IN IT.

AGE IS JUST YOUR SCORE ON THE DISTINGUISHED PEOPLE LIST.

Date : .... ♡♡♡♡♡♡♡

I AM BLESSED TO HAVE YOU IN MY LIFE. HAPPY BIRTHDAY

Date : ....

♡♡♡♡♡♡♡

GUESS WHAT? IT IS YOUR DAY TODAY. GO BE THE KING OF THE WORLD!

Date : .... ♡♡♡♡♡♡♡

YOU SUCK AT AGING! CAN YOU AT LEAST TRY TO LOOK OLDER?

Date : .... ♡♡♡♡♡♡♡

YOU'RE NOT GETTING OLDER... JUST MORE DISTINGUISHED! HAPPY BIRTHDAY.

Date : _____ ♡♡♡♡♡♡♡

CHEERS TO YOU FOR ANOTHER TRIP AROUND THE SUN!

Date : ....   ♡♡♡♡♡♡♡

MY WISH FOR YOU IS THAT YOU GET ALL OF YOUR BIRTHDAY WISHES THIS YEAR

Date : .... ♡♡♡♡♡♡♡

ON THIS WONDERFUL DAY, I WISH YOU THE BEST THAT LIFE HAS TO OFFER!

Date : .... ♡♡♡♡♡♡♡

IT'S ALWAYS A TREAT TO WISH HAPPY BIRTHDAY TO SOMEONE SO SWEET.

Date : ....

♡♡♡♡♡♡♡

ON YOUR BIRTHDAY I WISH YOU SUCCESS AND ENDLESS HAPPINESS!

Date : ....

♡♡♡♡♡♡♡

HAPPY BIRTHDAY TO THE BEST PRESENT THAT LIFE HAS GIVEN ME!

♡♡♡♡♡♡♡

MAY YOU BE HAPPY AND PROSPEROUS. I HOPE YOU HAVE A FABULOUS DAY!

Date : ....

♡♡♡♡♡♡♡

HAPPY BIRTHDAY! MAKE THIS A SPECIAL DAY TO REMEMBER.

Date : _____ ♡♡♡♡♡♡♡

MAY THE DREAMS OF YOUR BIRTHDAY MANIFEST INTO REALITY.

Date : .... ♡♡♡♡♡♡♡

EVERY DAY YOU SPARKLE BUT TODAY YOU RULE! HAPPY BIRTHDAY!

Date : ....

♡♡♡♡♡♡♡

MAY EVERYTHING BE HAPPY AND EVERYTHING BE BRIGHT

Date : .... ♡♡♡♡♡♡♡

I WISH YOU GOOD LUCK AND ENDLESS SUCCESS IN LIFE HAPPY BIRTHDAY

Date : .... ♡ ♡ ♡ ♡ ♡ ♡ ♡

WISHING YOU A MAGICAL BIRTHDAY FILLED WITH WONDERFUL SURPRISES AND FULL OF JOY

Date : .... ♡♡♡♡♡♡♡

MAY YOUR BIRTHDAY BE SPRINKLED WITH FUN AND LAUGHTER

Date : ....

♡ ♡ ♡ ♡ ♡ ♡ ♡

MAY ALL THE JOY YOU HAVE SPREAD AROUND COME BACK TO YOU A HUNDREDFOLD

Date : _____

♡♡♡♡♡♡♡

YOU ARE THE SWEETEST PERSON I KNOW, AND THIS BIRTHDAY IS A FRESH BEGINNING

Date : .... ♡♡♡♡♡♡♡

MAY THIS SPECIAL DAY BRING YOU ENDLESS JOY AND TONS OF PRECIOUS MEMORIES!

Date : .... ♡♡♡♡♡♡♡

YOU GET MORE AMAZING EVERY YEAR. HOPE YOUR BIRTHDAY IS, TOO!

Date : ....

♡♡♡♡♡♡♡

THANKS FOR ALWAYS BEING THERE AND MAKING LIFE FUN. WISH BIG TODAY!

Date : _____ ♡♡♡♡♡♡♡

THE WORLD IS SO LUCKY TO HAVE YOU IN IT, HERE'S TO A WONDERFUL YEAR AHEAD!

Date : ....

♡♡♡♡♡♡♡

DON'T LIGHT THE CANDLES BEFORE I ARRIVE! HAPPY BIRTHDAY AND SEE YOU TONIGHT!

Date : ....

♡♡♡♡♡♡♡

THE JOY IS IN THE AIR BECAUSE YOUR SPECIAL DAY IS HERE!

Date : ....

♡♡♡♡♡♡♡

HERE'S TO THE SWEETEST AND LOVELIEST PERSON I KNOW. HAPPY BIRTHDAY!

Date : ....

♡♡♡♡♡♡♡

FLY HIGH TO THE HAPPINESS AND WATCH YOUR DREAMS COME TRUE

Date : .... ♡♡♡♡♡♡♡

YOU'RE OLDER TODAY THAN YESTERDAY BUT YOUNGER THAN TOMORROW

Date : .... ♡♡♡♡♡♡♡

I CELEBRATE YOU TODAY BECAUSE YOU DESERVE EVERY BIT OF IT AND MORE

Date : .... ♡♡♡♡♡♡♡

I AM WISHING YOU AN AMAZING BETTER THAN THE ONE YOU'VE HAD BEFORE

Date : ....

♡♡♡♡♡♡♡

KEEP CALM AND STAY SAFE.... AND HAVE A VERY HAPPY BIRTHDAY!

Date : ....

♡ ♡ ♡ ♡ ♡ ♡ ♡

REMEMBER TO ALWAYS CHERISH THE WONDERFUL GIFT THAT IS LIFE

Date : .... ♡♡♡♡♡♡♡

I'D GIVE YOU THE STARS. BUT THEY DON'T SHINE AS BRIGHT AS YOU DO.

Date : ....

♡♡♡♡♡♡♡

I DON'T KNOW WHAT GIFT I CAN GIVE YOU BECAUSE YOU ARE THE BEST ONE.

Date : ....

♡ ♡ ♡ ♡ ♡ ♡ ♡

HOPE THE CANDLES ON YOUR CAKE LIGHT UP THE BEST SMILE I'VE SEEN

Date : ....

♡ ♡ ♡ ♡ ♡ ♡ ♡

CAN'T WAIT TO SPEND ALL THE FUTURE BIRTHDAYS WITH YOU

Date : ....

♡♡♡♡♡♡♡

YOU ARE THE HOTTEST NERD I'VE EVER SEEN. HAPPY BIRTHDAY.

Date : .... ♡♡♡♡♡♡♡

I DON'T CELEBRATE THE DAYS THAT MAKE YOU LOOK OLDER, EXCEPT FOR YOURS

Date : ....

♡♡♡♡♡♡♡

ANOTHER YEAR OLDER, ANOTHER REASON TO TELL YOU HOW SPECIAL YOU ARE.

Date : _____ ♡♡♡♡♡♡♡

JUMP IN, HEAD FIRST, WHENEVER YOU CAN. LIFE SHOULD BE AN ADVENTURE.

Date : ....

♡♡♡♡♡♡♡

YOU DESERVE ONLY THE BEST OF EVERYTHING TRUE AND GOOD!

Date : ....

♡♡♡♡♡♡♡

HAPPY BIRTHDAY. ENJOY THE RIDE TODAY AND THE JOURNEY FOREVER TOMORROW!

Date : .... ♡♡♡♡♡♡♡

You've always been a blessing and inspiration to everyone around you!

Date : ....

♡♡♡♡♡♡♡

YOU ARE A WONDERFUL PERSON. MAY YOU HAVE A WONDERFUL BIRTHDAY AND LIFE.

YOUR BIRTHDAY IS GOING TO BE SO GREAT. I'LL MAKE SURE OF IT.

Date : .... ♡♡♡♡♡♡♡

HAVE AN AMAZING BIRTHDAY TODAY AND AN EVEN MORE AMAZING YEAR.

Date : .... ♡ ♡ ♡ ♡ ♡ ♡ ♡

YOUR BIRTHDAY IS ONLY ONCE A YEAR, SO LET'S MAKE IT EPIC.

Date : .... ♡♡♡♡♡♡♡

LIFE IS SHORT, YOUR BIRTHDAY IS ALSO. ENJOY IT AT MAXIMUM. HAPPY BIRTHDAY!

Date : ....

♡♡♡♡♡♡♡

WORDS ALONE CANNOT EXPRESS THE HAPPINESS THAT I WISH FOR YOU ON THIS WONDERFUL DAY

Date : ....

♡♡♡♡♡♡♡

HAVE A FABULOUS DAY! TODAY IS YOUR TIME TO SHINE. HAPPY BIRTHDAY!

Date : .... ♡♡♡♡♡♡♡

HAPPY BIRTHDAY TO ONE OF THE NICEST PEOPLE I HAVE EVER MET

Date : ....

♡ ♡ ♡ ♡ ♡ ♡

MAY THE SUNSHINE BE THE BRIGHTEST AND THE BIRDS SING THE SWEETEST TODAY.

Date : ....

♡♡♡♡♡♡♡

TODAY IS NOT THE END OF ANOTHER YEAR BUT THE START OF A NEW ONE. HAPPY BADY.

Date : _____ ♡♡♡♡♡♡♡

ON THIS SPECIAL DAY, I WANT TO MAKE EACH AND EVERY SECOND OF YOUR BIRTHDAY MEMORABLE.

♡♡♡♡♡♡♡

YOU ARE REALLY DIFFERENT FROM THE WHOLE WORLD. FEEL BEAUTIFUL WITH YOU EVERY DAY

Date : ....

♡♡♡♡♡♡♡

HEY, FIRECRACKER! I HOPE YOU HAVE ONE BRIGHT AND SHINY DAY.

Date : ....

♡ ♡ ♡ ♡ ♡ ♡ ♡

YOUR PRESENCE IN MY LIFE HAS MADE IT COLORFUL AND GIVEN IT A NEW DIMENSION

Date : ....

♡♡♡♡♡♡♡

WITH THE NEW YEAR IN YOUR LIFE, YOU MAY ACHIEVE BIGGER THINGS. HAPPY BIRTHDAY.

Date : ....

♡♡♡♡♡♡♡

HAPPY BIRTHDAY TO SOMEONE WHO SHINES BRIGHTLY LIKE THE SUN.

Date : ....

♡♡♡♡♡♡♡

TODAY IS YOUR BIRTHDAY, BUT REMEMBER TO NOT GROW UP TOO FAST.

♡♡♡♡♡♡♡

TODAY IS A GIFT, NOT JUST FOR YOU, BUT FOR ALL WHO KNOW YOU.

Date : ....

♡ ♡ ♡ ♡ ♡ ♡ ♡

EVERY SINGLE YEAR YOU SEEM TO BE GETTING MORE AND MORE BEAUTIFUL.

Date : ....

FOR YOUR BIRTHDAY REMEMBER THAT A SMILE IS GOOD FOR CLEARING WRINKLES!

Date : .... ♡♡♡♡♡♡♡

EVERY HOUR, SECOND, AND MILLISECOND SHOULD BE SPENT LIVING LIFE TO THE FULLEST

Date : ....

♡♡♡♡♡♡♡

I WISH YOU ALL THAT YOU DESERVE: BEAUTIFUL GIFTS, HAPPINESS, JOY, AND LOTS OF MONEY!

Date : .... ♡♡♡♡♡♡♡

A WISE MAN ONCE SAID THAT A BIRTHDAY IS THE ONLY PROOF THAT WE HAVE THE CHANCE TO LIVE LONG

Date : ....

♡♡♡♡♡♡♡

WHEN YOU MAKE YOUR BIRTHDAY WISH, MAKE IT A REALLY GOOD ONE, AND IT WILL SURELY COME TRUE.

Date : _____ ♡♡♡♡♡♡♡

TODAY WE CELEBRATE THAT THERE IS A PERSON AS CUTE AND COOL AS YOU IN THIS WORLD

Date : ....

♡♡♡♡♡♡♡

MAY TODAY BE THE BEST BIRTHDAY YOU'VE EVER HAD. HAVE FUN ON YOUR SPECIAL DAY DEAR.

Date : .... ♡♡♡♡♡♡♡

LONG TIME AGO THE WORLD HAS BEEN GIVEN A WONDERFUL GIFT AND IT IS YOU

Date : ....

♡♡♡♡♡♡♡

I AM UMPTEEN MILES AWAY BUT MY HEART IS STILL HOVERING AT YOUR PARTY.

Date : ....

♡♡♡♡♡♡♡

LAST BUT NOT THE LEAST, YOU ARE ALWAYS MY PRICEST GIFT. HAPPY BIRTHDAY

Date : ....

♡♡♡♡♡♡♡

I WISH NOTHING YOU LOSE AND FIND WHAT YOU SEEK IN YOUR HEART

Date : .... ♡♡♡♡♡♡♡

MAY YOU HAVE THE SWEETNESS IN YOUR LIFE FOREVER! HAPPY BIRTHDAY

Date : .... ♡♡♡♡♡♡♡

NO WORDS CAN EXPRESS ALL THE RESPECT AND ADMIRATION THAT WE HAVE FOR YOU!